HAL LEONARD PIANO/VOCAL/GUITAR SERIES

The Good Ole Songs

CONTENTS

SENTIMENTAL JOURNEY

Em Ab9 G7 C F9 Fm6 C F
heart at ease,__ Gon - na make a Sen - ti - ment - al Jour - ney To re - new old
Em Adim G7 C
mem - o - ries.__ Got my bag, I got my res - er - va - tion, Spent each dime I
Em Ab9 G7 C F9 Fm6 C F
could af - ford.__ Like a child in wild an - ti - ci - pa - tion, Long to hear that
Em Adim G7 C Fdim F
"All a - board."__ Sev - en,____ that's the time we leave, at
mf

Cdim C C#7 D7
sev - en.___ I'll be wait - in' up for Heav - en,___
D9 G7 G6 Dm7 G6 Gdim G9 C
Count - in' ev - 'ry mile of rail - road track__ that takes me back.__ Nev - er thought my
mp
Em Ab9 G7 C
heart could be so "yearn - y." Why did I de - cide to roam?__ Got - ta take this
F9 Fm6 C F Em Adim G7 C Em Adim G7 C
Sen - ti - ment - al Jour - ney, Sen - ti - ment - al Jour - ney home.__ Jour - ney home.__
rit.

STORMY WEATHER
(KEEPS RAININ' ALL THE TIME)

Words by TED KOEHLER
Music by HAROLD ARLEN

Am7
D11
G
Am7
D7-9
G
Just can't get my poor self to-geth-er, I'm wear-y all the time, the
C
G G#dim
Am7
D7-9
G
Am7 G
C
time, So wear-y all the time. When {he she} went a-way the blues walked
mf
G
C
G
C
G
in and met me. If {he she} stays a-way old rock-in' chair will get me.
C
G
C
G
E7-5
All I do is pray the Lord a-bove will let me walk in the sun once

A7
D7-9
D7
G
G#dim
Am7
D9
more. Can't go on, ev-'ry-thing I had is gone, Storm-y
G
Am7
D11
G
Weath-er, Since my {man gal} and I ain't to-geth-er,
Am7
D7-9
G
Am7
D7-9
keeps rain-in' all the time, keeps rain-in' all the
1
G
Am7
D9
2
G
Am7
Gmaj7
C
G
time. Don't know time.
rall.
p
Ped.

SUNRISE SERENADE

Lyric by JACK LAWRENCE
Music by FRANKIE CARLE

C G7 G9 C C9
Look at the buds you can al-most see how they're break-in' thru; Look at the birds feed-in' all their young in the sy-ca-mores
F D9 D7 G9 Gdim G9 G7 G9
But you bet-ter get on with your morn-in' chores. Just take a breath of that new-mown hay and the su-gar cane;
C G7 G9 C Cdim
looks like to-night there should be a moon down in lov-er's lane. There you go day-dream-ing when it's
C Bb7 A7 Eb9 D9 Ab9 G9 G11 1 C C+ 2 C
time that you o-beyed that Sun - rise Ser - e - nade. Good
ped.

TENDERLY

Lyric by JACK LAWRENCE
Music by WALTER GROSS

Cm7 F7 Bb7 Ebmaj7
lost in a sigh were we. The shore was kissed by sea and
Bb+ Ebm7 Ab9 Fm7
mist Ten - der - ly. I can't for - get how two hearts
Abm Eb Gm7 Fm7 Eb Abm Bb7 Bdim
met breath - less - ly. Your arms op - ened wide and
Dm7 Ebm F9 F#dim Eb C+ Fm7 Abm E7
closed me in - side; You took my lips, you took my love so Ten - der -
rall.
1 Eb Ab Bbsus Bb7
ly The eve - ning
2 Eb
ly.

I'LL WALK ALONE

(From "Follow The Boys")

Lyric by SAMMY CAHN
Music by JULE STYNE

F6
E7
Am7
D7
F6
E7
why and I'll tell them I'd rath - er;
There are dreams I must gath-
A7
D7
G
er,
Dreams we fash-ioned the night
you held me
Dm7
G7
C
Cm
tight.
I'll al - ways be near you,
wher - ev - er you are
Each
Gmaj7
Em7
F#7
night in ev - 'ry prayer.
If you call I'll hear you, no

Em7
F#7
Bm7
E7
A7
D7
mat - ter how far; just close your eyes and I'll be there. Please walk a -
G
F6
E7
Am7
lone and send your love and your kiss - es to guide me.
D7
F6
E7
A7
D7
G#dim
Am7
D7
Till you're walk - ing be - side me, I'll Walk A -
1
G6
A7
D7
2
G6
lone. I'll Walk A - lone.

OLE BUTTERMILK SKY
(From "Canyon Passage")

Lyric and Music by
HOAGY CARMICHAEL and JACK BROOKS

Fm
Bb7
Bb11
Eb
Ab
Eb
Eb7
Christ - mas tree, Head - in' for the one I love. I'm gon - na pop 'er the
Ab
Eb9
Eb7
Ab
Bb7
Eb7
ques - tion, that ques - tion, "Do you, dar - lin', do you do?" It - 'll be
f
Ab
Abm
Eb
F9
F7
Bb7
Ab
Bb7
eas - y, so eas - y If I can on - ly bank on you. Ole But - ter - milk
mp
Eb
Ab
Eb
Ab
Eb
Bb11
Bb7
Sky, I'm tell - ing you why; now you know. Keep it in
Eb
Fm
Eb
Bb11
Bb7
Eb
Bb9+5
mind to - night, Keep a - brush - ing those clouds from sight. Ole But - ter - milk
mf

Eb
Ab
Eb
Sky, Don't you fail me when I'm need-in' you most. Hang a moon a-bove her
Fm
Bb7
Ab
Eb
Ab
Eb
Bb9+5
hitch-ing post; Hitch me to the one I love. You can if you
Eb
Ab
Eb
F7
try, Don't tell me no lie. Will you be mel-low and bright to-night,
Bb11
Bb13
1 Eb
Bb7
Ab
Bb7
2 Eb
Ab
Eb
but-ter-milk sky? Ole But-ter-milk sky?
mp
f

IT'S SO NICE TO HAVE A MAN AROUND THE HOUSE

Lyric by JACK ELLIOTT
Music by HAROLD SPINA

3rd Chorus

It's So Nice To Have A Man Around The House,
Oh, so nice to have a man around the house,
Just a hero bold and vicious,
Who'll insist he get his wishes,
Oh, but first he'll do the dishes. . .It's so nice.
Oh, a house is just a house without a man,
He's the necessary evil in your plan;
Just a knight in shining armor,
Who is something of a charmer,
Though it's two to one you wind up with a louse,
It's So Nice To Have A Man Around The House.

4th Chorus

It's So Nice To Have A Man Around The House,
Oh, so nice to have a man around the house,
Just a guy who is attentive,
And who has a strong incentive,
To be more or less inventive. . .It's so nice.
Oh, a house is just a house without a man,
He's the necessary evil in your plan,
So put no one else above him,
When you love him really love him,
Even though he may be someone'else's spouse,
It's So Nice To Have A Man Around The House.

A BUSHEL AND A PECK
(From "Guys and Dolls")

By FRANK LOESSER

Light Bounce Tempo

A7-9 F#7-9 G D+ Dm D+
a - bout you 'Cause
G D7 G D7 G D7
I love you A Bu - shel And A Peck y' bet your pur - ty neck I do
G D7 G7 C
Doo - dle oo - dle oo - dle Doo - dle oo - dle oo - dle a
G D7 1 G D7 2 G
doo - dle oo - dle oo - dle ooo.
8va

JOEY, JOEY, JOEY

(From "The Most Happy Fella")

Mystically

By FRANK LOESSER

2
E
F/E
E
Eb/F
Db/F
Fmaj7
F6/9
gone.
That's what the wind
5
3
3
f
C
Cmaj7
C6/G
Dm
A
Dm7
G/D
sings to me
When the bunk I've been bunk-in' in gets to feel-in' too
mf
Am
Am
Dm
A
Dm7
E7
soft and co-zy
When the grub they've been cook-in' me gets to tast-in' too
Am
Am6
Am7
C
G/D
G+/D#
Cmaj7/E
D11
D9
good.
When I've had all I want of the la-dies in the neigh-bor-

G
Dm7
G9
G7-9
Cmaj9
C6
Cmaj7
C6
hood,
She sings,
Jo - ey,
Jo - ey,
Cmaj9
C6
Cmaj7
C6
C9
C+
Gb-5/C
C+
C9
C+
Jo - ey,
Jo - ey,
Jo - ey, Joe.
accel. (subito)
Gb-5/C
C+
Cmaj7
C6/G
Cmaj9
C6
Cmaj7
C6/G
Cmaj9
C6/G
You've been too long
in one place,
And it's
mf
Eb+/G
B7+5
Am7-5/C
B7-5/F
B7+5(b9)
E
E/F
F
E/F
Eb/F
D/F
Db/F
Cmaj7
C
time to go,
Time to go!
Jo - ey,
rit.
f
Db7
Db7(#9)
C
Jo - ey, Joe!
molto rit.
sfz

ON A SLOW BOAT TO CHINA

By FRANK LOESSER

C7
Gm7
C9
Cm7
Gb9
F9
Leave all your lovers
(lovlies)
Weep-ing on the far a-way shore.
Bb
Dm7
G7
Out on the brin-y with a
Cm
C#dim
Bb
moon big and shin-y,
Melt-ing your
D7
Eb
Cm
Dm7
G7
heart of stone,

Cm7
Ab7
A7
Bb
Ab7
G7
I'd love to get you On A Slow Boat To Chi-na,
f
C7
Cm7
B7
To Coda
Bb
Cm7
F9+5
All to my-self a-lone.
Bb
Bb
Eb
Edim
lone. There is no verse so this song, 'Cause I don't
mf
Bb
Edim
Eb
Cm7
F7
D.S. al Coda
want to wait a mo-ment too long To say that
CODA
Bb
Cm7
F7+5
Bb
lone.
ff

IT'S AN OLD FASHIONED WALTZ

Words and Music by MILTON SCHAFER

Am7 D7 G7 Dm7 G7
gain. Makes me think of the days when
C Cm6 Gsus G A7
Grand - ma wore bus - tles And Grand - pa pro - posed on his
Am7 D7 G C6 Cm
knees. It's An Old Fash - ioned Waltz and for an
G Bm7 E7 Bm7 E7 Am7 D7
old fash - ioned waltz, Will you do me the hon - or,
G C#dim D7sus D7 G G
please? It's An please?

ANGRY

Words by DUDLEY MECUM
Music by JULES CASSARD,
HENRY BRUNIES and MERRIT BRUNIES

C7
F7
Bb7
love you true.
some - one new.
Just be - cause I took a look at
Don't be - lieve a word you hear just
Eb
Ebm
some - bod - y else
wait till you see
That's no rea - son you should put poor
Then you'll find no cause to show you're
Gb7
Bb
me on the shelf.
jeal - ous of me.
An - gry please don't be
an - gry 'cause I was on - ly teas - ing
you.
you.

WONDERFUL COPENHAGEN
(From "Hans Christian Andersen")

By FRANK LOESSER

Dm G7 C F
down. To Won - der - ful, Won - der - ful Co - pen -
G7 C Cmaj7 A7-9
ha - gen, sal - ty old queen of the sea
A7 Dm7 G7 C Em
Once I sailed a - way, But I'm home to - day, sing - ing
Am Em Am E+ D7
Co - pen - ha - gen, Won - der - ful, Won - der - ful Co - pen -
G7 1 C G7 2 C
ha - gen for me. me.

PRISONER OF LOVE

Words and Music by LEO ROBIN,
CLARENCE GASKILL and RUSS COLUMBO

Fm
Gm
Eb
Db9
Eb
Am7-5
D7
I can't es-cape, for it's too late now,
I'm just a Pris-'ner Of Love.
What's the
Gm
D7
mf-f
good of my car-ing, if some-one is shar-ing Those arms with me?
Al-though
cresc.
G
D7
Bb7
he
she
has an-oth-er, I can't have an-oth-er; For I'm not free.
Fm7
A7
Bb7
C9
he's
she's
in my dreams, a-wake or sleep-ing,
Up-on my knees to
him
her
I'm creep-ing;
1
2
Cm7
Fm7-5
My ver-y life is in
his
her
keep-ing,
I'm just a Pris-'ner Of Love.
Love.
f
fz

THE MOON OF MANAKOORA

(From "The Hurricane")

Lyric by FRANK LOESSER
Music by ALFRED NEWMAN

Ab
Fm7-5
Eb
Ebmaj7
Eb7
Moon Of Man-a-koo - ra soon will rise a-
Ab
Fm7-5
Eb
Eb6
Bb
gain A-bove the is - land shore Then I'll be-hold it
B7
Bb7
Db
Dm7-5
Bb
in your dusk - y eyes and you'll be in my
B7
Bb7
1
Eb
Eb7
2
Eb6
arms once more. The more.

HOOP-DEE-DOO

Words by FRANK LOESSER
Music by MILTON DeLUGG

Eb
this kind of mus - ic is like heav - en to me.
Hoop - dee - doo, Hoop - dee - doo,
Eb7
Ab
To Coda
It's got me high - er than a kite.
Eb
C9
Hand me down my soup and fish, I am gon - na get my wish

Fm7
Fdim
Bb7sus
Bb7
Eb
Hoop - dee - doo - in' it to - night.
When there's a
Trio
Ab
Fm
Cm
Ab
trom - bone play - in' rah - ta dah - dah - dah, I get a
mp
Bdim
Eb7
thrill I al - ways will.
When there's a
mp
Bbm7
Eb7
Bbm7
Eb7
Bbm7
Eb7
con - cer - tin - a stretch - in' out a mile I al - ways

Bbm7
Eb7
Ab6
smile, 'cause that's my style. When there's a
Ab
Fm
Cm
Ab
fid - dle in the mid - dle and he plays the tune so sweet,
cresc.
Ab7
Db6
Plays the tune so sweet that I could die.
Ab
F7
Lead me to the floor, and hear me yell for more 'cause I'm a
fz
fz
Bb7
Eb9
Eb7
Ab
Bb7
hoop - dee - doo - in' kind of guy.

Eb
D.S. al Coda
f
CODA
Ab
Eb
C9
I'm in clo - ver I'm in bloom, when I'm danc - in' give me room
Fm7
Fdim
Bb7sus
Bb7
Eb7
D7
Db7
C7
Hoop - dee - doo - in' it with all of my might,
Fm
Ab
Eb
C9
Rain may fall and snow may come, Noth - in's gon - na stop me from
Fm7
Fdim
Bb7sus
Bb7
Eb
Hoop - dee - doo - in' it to - night.
fz

WHAT ARE YOU DOING NEW YEAR'S EVE

F
Eb7
F
May- be it's much too ear - ly in the game, Ah, but I thought I'd
Won-der whose arms will hold you good and tight, When it's ex - act - ly
mp
Bb
Bbm
F
Dm7
G7
ask you just the same, What are you do - ing New Year's,
twelve - 'o-clock that night. Wel-com-ing in the New Year,
1
C7
F
Gm7
Gb9
2
C7
Gm9
C7-9
F
E7-9
New Year's Eve? New Year's Eve.
Am
D7
Fm
Bb9
Am
May- be I'm cra - zy to sup - pose I'd ev - er be the

Bm7-5
Bb9
Am
D9
G7
G9
one you chose
Out of the thou-sand
in - vi - ta - tions
you'll
re -
C7
F#dim
C7
F
Eb7
ceive.
Ah, but in case I
stand one lit - tle chance,
F
Bb
Bbm
F
Dm7
Here comes the jack - pot
ques - tion in ad - vance,
What Are You Do - ing
G7
C9
Gm9
C7-9
F
Bdim
Bbm
C7
F
Bb
F
New
Year's,
New
Year's
Eve?
Eve?
rall.

NO TWO PEOPLE
(From "Hans Christian Andersen")

Medium Schottische

By FRANK LOESSER

F7
Fm7
Bb7-5
Bb7
Eb
C7-9
Fm
Abm6
love, it's in - cre - di - ble; No Two Peo - ple have ev - er been so in love as
been so in love. Been so as
Eb
Abmaj7
Eb
Bb
Eb
Ab
Bb
Eb
my lov - ey dove and This is u - nique, the pos - i - tive peak, oh,
my lov - ey dove and I.
Cm
Fm
Bb7
Eb
C7
we are the most un - u - su - al cou - ple on earth.
No Two Peo - ple have ev - er

Fm
Abm6
Eb
Cm
F7
Fm7
Bb7-5
Bb7
Mooned such a moon, Juned such a June. What he means is that
mooned such a moon, Juned such a June, spooned such a spoon.
Eb
C7-9
Fm
Abm6
Eb
Abmaj7
Eb
Bb7
No Two Peo-ple have ev - er been so in tune as my ma - ca-roon and
Been so as my ma - ca-roon and
Eb
Eb7
Ab
Bb7
Ebmaj7
Cm
C7
I. And when we kiss, well it's like this,
I. And when we kiss, and when we kiss, well it's his-

F7 Fdim C7 F7 Bb7
Guitar Tacet
let me tell it.
to - ri - cal, it's hys - te - ri - cal, well cer - tain - ly dar - ling.
Eb C7-9 Fm Abm6 Eb Cm
No Two Peo-ple have ev - er been so in love, been so in love,
Been so in love, been so in
F7 Fm7 Bb7 Eb C7 Fm Abm6
been so in love. Been so as
love, it's im - pos - si - ble; No Two Peo-ple have ev - er been so in love as

Eb
Abmaj7
Eb
Bb
Eb
Ab
Bb
Eb
my lov - ey dove and This is the cream, the ve - ry ex- treme, the
my lov - ey dove and I.
Cm
Fm
Bb7
Eb
C7
sort of a dream you could - n't i - ma - gine at all.
Well an - y - way, No Two Peo - ple have ev - er
Fm
Abm6
Eb
Abmaj7
Eb
Bb7
Eb
Been so as my lov - ey dove and I.
been so in love as my lov - ey dove and I.

I BELIEVE IN YOU

(From "How To Succeed In Business Without Really Trying")

By FRANK LOESSER

G
D
G
Cmaj7
Db7
D7
G
You,
I Be - lieve In You.
R.H.
G#dim
G
Eb7
Ab
Bbm7
Eb7-5
Ab
I hear the
And when my faith in my fel - low man
Bbm7
Db9
Cm7
F7
Bb
Cm7
F7
all but falls a - part,
I've but to feel your hand
Bb
Gm7
C7
D7sus
D7
G#dim
grasp - ing mine and I take heart, I take heart.
To see the
rit.

Am7 D9 C C#m7 F#7 Bm C

cool clear eyes of a seek-er of wis-dom and truth,

Bm G#dim Am7 D9 C C#m7 F#7

Yet there's that slam bang tang rem - i - nis-cent of gin and ver -

B C B Cmaj7 Db7 D7 G

mouth. Oh I Be - lieve In You,

Cmaj7 Db7 D7 Cmaj7 D11 Gmaj7

I Be - lieve In You.

R.H.

BABY, IT'S COLD OUTSIDE
(From "Neptune's Daughter")

By FRANK LOESSER

F9
Bb6
nice
warm
My moth - er will start to wor - ry
And
My sis - ter will be sus - pi - cious
My
I'll hold your hands They're just like ice.
Beau - ti - ful, what's your
Look out the win - dow at that storm
Gosh, your lips look de -
Bb9
F6
fath - er will be pac - ing the floor
So real - ly I'd bet - ter
broth - er will be there at the door
My maid - en aunt's mind is
hur - ry?
Lis - ten to the fi - re-place roar!
li - cious
Waves up - on a trop - i - cal shore!
Gm7
C7
scur - ry.
Well, may - be just a half a drink more
The
vi - cious
Well, may - be just a ci - ga-rette more
I've
Beau - ti - ful, please, don't hur - ry
Put some re - cords on while I pour
Gosh, your lips are de - li - cious
Nev - er such a bliz - zard be - fore

F
Gm7
C7
neigh - bors might think
Say, What's in this drink?
got to get home
Say, lend me a comb
But, ba - by, it's bad out there
No cabs to be had
But, ba - by, you'd freeze out there
It's up to your knees
Gm7
C7
F
I wish I knew how to break the
You've real - ly been grand but don't you
out there
Your eyes are like star - light now
out there
I thrill when you touch my hand
F9
B♭6
spell
I ought to say "No, no,
see
There's bound to be talk to -
I'll take your hat your hair looks swell
How can you do this thing to me

Gm7
C7
no, Sir!"
At least I'm gon - na say that I tried
I
mor - row.
At least there will be plen - ty im - plied
I
Mind if I move in clos - er?
What's the sense of hurt - ing my pride
Think of my life - long sor - row
If you caught pneu-mo - nia and died
F
Eb7
D7
G7
C7
real - ly can't stay
Ah, but it's cold out -
real - ly can't stay
Ah, but it's cold out -
Oh, ba - by, don't hold out,
Ba - by, It's Cold Out -
Get o - ver that old doubt,
Ba - by, It's Cold Out -
1
F6
C7
2
F6
side.
I
side.
side.
side.
3

ONE FOR MY BABY
(AND ONE MORE FOR THE ROAD)
(From "The Sky's The Limit")

Lyric by JOHNNY MERCER
Music by HAROLD ARLEN

G7+5
Cm7
Fm7
Gm
Abmaj7
Bb11
Eb6
D7
D7+5
One For My Ba - by and one more for the road.
I
R.H.
G
D
G
D
G7
got the rou - tine, so drop an - oth - er nick - el in the ma - chine, I'm
mp
pp
3
G
D
G
Dm7
G7
feel - in' so bad, I wish you'd make the mu - sic dream - y and sad, Could
3
C
G
C
G
tell you a lot, But you've got to be true to your code, Make it

B7+5
Em7
Am7
Gmaj7
Cmaj7
D11
G
F#7
G9
One For My Ba - by and one more for the road. You'd
mf
Gm7
C7
Gm7/C
Cm7-5
C9
B7+5
E9
A9
D11
G
Am7
Bb6
Am7
nev - er know it, But Bud-dy, I'm a kind of po - et and I've got-ta lot - ta things to say, And
Gm7
C7
Gm7/C
Cm7-5
C9
Gm7
Eb9
D7+5
when I'm gloom-y, You sim - ply got-ta lis-ten to me, Un - til it's talked a - way, Well,
G
D
G
D
G7
that's how it goes And Joe, I know you're get - ting anx - ious to close, So,
pp
3

G
D
G
G
Dm7
G7
thanks for the cheer, I hope you did-n't mind my bend-ing your ear, This
C
G
C
G
torch that I've found, Must be drowned or it soon might ex-plode, Make it
B7+5
Em7
Am7
Gmaj7
Cmaj7
D11
B7+5
B7
E7-9
A7
D11
D7-9
G
One For My Ba-by and one more for the road, That long, long road.
R.H.
F9
Bb11
Bb7+5
G
Am7
G
G6
I road.
R.H.
mp
p
pp
ppp

STANDING ON THE CORNER
(From "The Most Happy Fella")

By FRANK LOESSER

Gmaj7 Bm7 Am7 Ab7 Gmaj7 Am7-5 Adim D7
To Coda
stand- ing on the cor- ner watch-ing all the girls, watch- ing all the girls, watch- ing all the girls go
Gmaj7 Am7 Bb7 B7 Em Em/D# Em/D A7/C#
by.
I'm the cat that got the cream,
Sat- ur-day, and I'm so broke,
Cmaj7 Bb Am7 D7 Em B/D#
Have- n't got a girl,
Could- n't buy a girl
But I can dream,
a nick- el coke.
Have- n't got a girl,
Still I'm liv-ing like
Em Eb7 G D7(+9) G D7(+9) G D9
But I can wish, so I take me down to Main Street And that's where I se-lect my i- mag- i- na- ry dish!
A mil- lion-aire, when I take me down to Main Street And I re- view the ha-rem pa- rad- ing for me there.
1. Eb7 D7
2. Eb7 D7
D.S. al Coda
CODA
Gmaj7 Ebmaj7 Abmaj7 Gmaj7 (add E)
by.
D.S. al Coda

YOU MADE ME LOVE YOU
(I DIDN'T WANT TO DO IT)

Words by JOE McCARTHY
Music by JAMES V. MONACO

E♭dim Dm7 Dm7-5 G7 Dm7 Dm7-5 G7 Dm7 B7+5 B7
sigh for, I did-n't wan-na tell you, I did-n't wan-na tell you, I want some love that's
E7 A7 Gm A7 Gm A7 Gm A7
true, yes, I do, 'deed I do, you know I do. Gim - me, gim - me what I cry— for, you
D7 Am7 D7 D7-5 C G♯dim Am Dm7 G7
know you got the brand of kiss-es that I die— for, You know You Made— Me— Love
1 C Cdim Dm7 G7-9
You.
2 C Fm C6/9
You.
rit.

IT'S BEEN A LONG, LONG TIME

Lyric by SAMMY CAHN
Music by JULE STYNE

C9
C7
Gm
Gm(+7)
Gm7
C7
Time. Have-n't felt like this, my dear, Since can't re-mem-ber when, It's Been A
Gm7
C9+5
F
Am7-5
D7
Long, Long Time. You'll nev-er know how man-y dreams I dreamed a-bout you Or
Gm
Gm7-5
C7
F
Fmaj7
just how emp-ty they all seemed with-out you. So, kiss me once, then kiss me twice, Then
Am7
D7
Gm7
C7
F
A♭dim
C7
C9
F
F6
kiss me once a-gain, It's Been A Long, Long Time. Just Time.
mf
sfz

AFTER YOU'VE GONE

By CREAMER & LAYTON

C7
F
F#dim
Loved you night and day;
How can you leave me, can't you
C
D9
G7
C
C+
see my tears?
List - en while I say:
Chorus
F
Dm7-5
C
A7
Af - ter you've gone, and left me cry - ing; Af - ter you've gone, There's no de - ny - ing;
Af - ter I'm gone, af - ter we break up; Af - ter I'm gone, You're gon - na wake up;
p mf
D9
G7
C
you'll feel blue, You'll feel sad, You'll miss the dear - est pal you've
you will find, You were blind, To let some - bod - y come and

C7
F
Dm7-5
C
ev - er had;
There'll come a time,
now don't for - get it,
There'll come a time,
change your mind;
Af - ter the years,
we've been to - geth - er,
Their joy and tears,
A7
Dm
A7
Dm
Dm7-5
when you'll re - gret it;
Some day,
when you grow lone - ly,
all kinds of weath - er;
Some day,
blue and down heart - ed,
C
E7
Am
D7
C
Your heart will break like mine and you'll want me on - ly,
Af - ter You've Gone,
You'll long to be with me right back where you start - ed;
Af - ter I'm gone,
G7
C
1
2
Af - ter You've Gone a - way.
Af - ter I'm gone a - way.

THERE WILL NEVER BE ANOTHER YOU

(From "Iceland")

Eb
Dm7
G7
There will be man - y oth - er nights like this, And
p-
mf
Cm
Bbm7
Eb7
I'll be stand - ing here with some - one new, There
Ab
Abm
Eb
Cm
will be oth - er songs to sing, An - oth - er fall, an - oth - er spring, But
F7
Bb11
Bb7
There Will Nev - er Be An - oth - er You. There

Eb
Dm7
G7
will be oth - er lips that I may kiss, But
Cm
Bbm7
Eb7
they won't thrill me like yours used to do, Yes,
Ab
Abm
Eb
G7
Cm
F7sus
F7
Ebdim
I may dream a mil - lion dreams, But how can they come true, If
Eb
D7
Bb7
Eb7
Fm7
Bb11
Bb7
1
Eb
2
Eb
there will nev - er ev - er be an - oth - er you? There you?
L.H.

LINDA

Words and Music by JACK LAWRENCE

A7 D7 G
Think of all the lov-in' I've missed. We pass on the street, my heart skips a beat, I
E7 Am7 D7
say to my-self "Hel-lo, Lin - da." If on-ly she'd smile I'd stop her a while And
G G7 C G
then I would get to know Lin - da. But mir-a - cles still hap-pen And
F E7 Am7 D7
when my luck-y star be-gins to shine, With one luck-y break I'll make Lin - da
1 G G#dim Am7 D7
mine. When
2 G G#dim Am D7 G6
mine.

ONCE IN LOVE WITH AMY

(From "Where's Charley?")

By FRANK LOESSER

C G Am7 G B7 E7 Am7 D9
po- et-ry and flow-ers, Moon a mil- lion hours a- way. You might be quite the fick- le heart- ed
Gmaj7 C7 Gmaj7 C9 Gmaj7 E9 Am7 D9 Gmaj7
ro- ver, So care- free and bold Who loves a girl and la- ter thinks it o- ver And
D A7 D7 G G#dim Am7 D7 G G#dim
just quits cold, But Once In Love With A-my, Al-ways in love with
Am7 D7 G C G Am7 G
A-my. Ev-er and ev-er sweet- ly you'll ro-mance 'er. Trou- ble is, the an-swer will
B7 E7 Am7 A9 D7 G
be That A- my'd rath- er stay in love with me.

MAY THE GOOD LORD BLESS AND KEEP YOU

Moderately

By MEREDITH WILLSON

C#dim Dm C#dim Dm7 G7 G+ C6 C#dim G7
wait - ed gold - en day to - day. May your
oth - ers shine on you to - day. May your
C F Dm7 G7 G7+5
trou - bles all be small ones, and your for - tune ten times
heart stay tuned to mus - ic that will cheer the hearts of
C A7 C#dim Dm C#dim Dm7
ten. May The Good Lord Bless And Keep You till we
men. May The Good Lord Bless And Keep You till we
G7 C F
meet a - gain. May you walk with sun - light
meet a - gain. May you long re - call the
3

C
F
shin - ing, and a blue - bird in ev - 'ry
rain - bows, then you'll soon for - get the
C
F
C
tree. May there be a sil - ver lin - ing back of
rain. May the warm and ten - der mem - 'ries be the
Am7
D9
Dm7
G7
C
ev - 'ry cloud you see.
ones that will re - main.
Fill your dreams with sweet to -
F
Dm7
G7
G7+5
C
mor - rows. Nev - er mind what might have been. May the

A7 C#dim Dm C#dim Dm7 G7
Good Lord Bless And Keep You till we meet a -
C G7 G+ C6 C#dim G7
gain. May The meet a - gain. May The
C E7+5 Fdim F6 F#dim C6 C#dim
Good Lord Bless And Keep You till we meet till we
Dm7 G7 C Db9 C
meet a - gain.
ritard.
Slowly

IF I WERE A BELL
(From "Guys and Dolls")

By FRANK LOESSER